Bumblebees

First published in 2002 by *Osmia* Publications, Banbury, UK

ISBN 0-9539906-7-2

A CIP record for this title is available from the British Library.

Cover Photograph: *Bombus hortorum*, Small garden bumblebee on a primrose *Primula vulgaris* in springtime
© Ken Preston-Mafham, Premaphotos Wildlife.

Production by *Osmia* Publications

Designed by Louisa Stevens

Printed and bound in Thailand by Gift Export Co. Ltd

About the Author

Chris O'Toole has been studying wild bees for more than thirty years. He heads the Bee Systematics and Biology Unit of the Hope Entomological Collections of the Oxford University Museum of Natural History and is the author of many books on insect natural history, including (with Anthony Raw), *Bees of the World.*

He is also a frequent broadcaster on radio and has been involved in the production of many television programmes in natural history, most notably *Alien Empire,* for which he wrote the accompanying book of the same name.

His research interests include the nesting biology of solitary bees and the systematics, biogeography and floral relations of Mediterranean bees. His most recently published book is *The Red Mason Bee: taking the sting out of beekeeping,* a practical guide to managing *Osmia rufa* as a pollinator in gardens, allotments and orchards.

Ongoing research on bumblebees includes a study of the functional morphology of the male genitalia.

Chris O'Toole is the founder of the Oxford Bee Company, a spin-out company of Oxford University. The company markets nests for mason bees (*Osmia* spp.), bumblebees and ladybirds and distributes books.

Acknowledgements

I thank my wife Rose for her constant support and encouragement. I am also grateful to my old friend and colleague, Prof. Tony Raw, for many stimulating conversations about bees over the years and for his helpful comments on the manuscript of this book.

I thank my brother Peter for several excellent photographs and Rod and Ken Preston-Mafham of Premaphotos Wildlife for their fine camera work.

Contents

The Color Plates

Plate 1

Bombus terrestris, *Buff-tailed bumblebee worker with well filled pollen baskets on knapweed. © Ken Preston-Mafham, Premaphotos Wildlife.*

Plate 2

Bombus pascuorum, *Common carder bumblebee worker visiting a flower of foxglove* Digitalis purpurea, *whose pollen heavily coats the top of the bees thorax. © Ken Preston-Mafham, Premaphotos Wildlife.*

Plate 3

Bombus hortorum, *Small garden bumblebee with loaded pollen baskets on a garden nasturtium*, Trapaeolum sp. *© Dr Rod Preston-Mafham, Premaphotos Wildlife.*

Plate 4

Plate 5

Plate 6

Misumena vatia, Flower spider (Thomisidae) female feeding on a bumblebee on common cow wheat. *© Ken Preston-Mafham, Premaphotos Wildlife.*

Plate 7

Bombus lucorum, *White-tailed bumblebee queen carrying phoretic deutonymphs of mite* Parasitellus fucorum. *© Ken Preston-Mafham, Premaphotos Wildlife.*

Plate 8

Volucella bombylans, *Bumblebee plume-horn, a hover fly (*Syrphidae*), a white-tailed bumblebee mimic. © Ken Preston-Mafham, Premaphotos Wildlife.*

Plate 9

Psithyrus bohemicus, *Female cuckoo bumblebee breaking open brood cell of host*, Bombus lucorum, *in order to lay eggs. © Peter O'Toole.*

Plate 10

Bombus lucorum, *White-tailed bumblebee drinking from the surface of a pond on a hot day. © Ken Preston-Mafham, Premaphotos Wildlife.*

Plate 11

Bombus pascuorum, *Common carder bumblebee worker pushing open the hinge of a garden Snapdragon* (Antirrhinum) *flower in the garden. © Ken Preston-Mafham, Premaphotos Wildlife.*

Plate 12

Oxford Bee Company Ltd, Bumblebee Nest

ONE

Background to the Bees

What are bees?

Bees are special kinds of hunting wasps that have become vegetarians: instead of catching insect prey as a source of protein for their larvae, they gather pollen from flowers. Flowers and bees have developed a mutual dependency over evolutionary time and this relationship has become fundamental to the ecology of the rest of life on earth. This is true for we humans, to the dramatic extent that much of the visual impact of natural habitats that we value depends on it. Even more dramatic is the fact that every third mouthful of human food depends on the unmanaged pollination services of bees.

Bumblebees (*Bombus* spp.) are social and live in colonies. When fully developed, each colony comprises a single, egg-laying female, the queen, and a number of sterile females called workers. A successful colony will go on to produce a new generation of queens and number of males.

There are anything between 20 and 30,000 bee species in the world. Britain has 254 species, 24 of them bumblebees, including six that live as cuckoos in the nests of other bumblebees; central Europe has about 750 species of bees, including about 70 bumblebees. Warm, dry regions are diversity hotspots for bees and the Mediterranean region, for example, probably has nearly 2000 species. I say 'probably' because we are still finding new, undescribed species and many Mediterranean areas have been poorly surveyed for bees.

Bumblebees, however, are typical of cooler, temperate climates and occur throughout Europe, Asia and North America. Some species are adapted to live at high altitudes in the Himalayas and the arctic areas of North America and Eurasia have 22 species. Two of these, *Bombus hyperboreus* and *B. polaris,* live well within the Arctic Circle, only 880km from the North Pole. A few species live in the forests of tropical Central and South America and some penetrate into the southern, colder parts of South America along the Andes. A few species live in North Africa, but bumblebees are absent from Africa south of the Sahara.

Unlike bumblebees, the vast majority of bees are solitary, rather than social. That is, each nest is the work of a single female working alone and there is no caste of sterile females or workers. Very many of these solitary species are called mining bees because they excavate nests in the ground. Female mining bees line their nest cells with a waterproof glandular secretion. Others, especially the mason and leaf-cutter bees, use pre-existing cavities such as hollow plant stems, snail shells or beetle borings in dead wood and, instead of lining their nest cells with glandular secretions, they use, according to species, gathered materials such as mud, resin, plant hairs, leaf pieces or a mastic of chewed leaves. Some species even use a combination of two or more of these building substances.

The wasp inheritance

The wasps that gave rise to the bees are not the familiar, black and yellow social papermaking wasps. These, the bane of summer picnics, belong to the family Vespidae. The progenitors of the bees were members of a large family of solitary hunting wasps comprising the Sphecidae, which has several thousand modern species, and which is found in most parts of the world.

Wasp or bee, a nesting female has to be able to find her way back to the nest after a hunting or pollen-gathering trip. Bees inherited from their wasp ancestors the ability to memorize both near and distant landmarks relative to the nest entrance. They also inherited another vital skill: sun-compass orientation. A female bee memorizes the position of the sun relative to her nest entrance when she leaves on a foraging trip. This might seem at first sight to be a rather risky way of doing things. After all, the sun has an irritating habit of moving across the sky. But wasps and bees have sorted this one: they have an in-built clock which compensates for the sun's movements.

And what if clouds obscure the sun? Well, this does not faze these insects: unlike us, their eyes can detect the plane of polarized light, so they know where the sun is, even if we don't.

After finding a nest site, a female bee makes several orientation flights, which have a characteristic looping from side-to-side pattern around the nest entrance. At this stage, she is memorising landmarks close to the entrance. These may be a pale stone marked with a patch of lichen and, say, a clump of flowers. During the course of her orientation flight, the bee will broaden the sweep of her looping flight pattern as she begins to memorize more distant landmarks, for example, an isolated tree and the shape of a far hill.

In this way, she builds up a mental map of the immediate surroundings of her nest which includes both near and distant cues. This, combined with the ability to detect the plane of polarized light and compensate for the movement of the sun, gives the female bee a very efficient way of finding her way around her part of the world. Just how efficient this is can be judged from the fact that those close relatives of the bumblebees, the orchid bees of Central and South America, can find their way home after foraging trips of 30-40km. Experiments in Oxfordshire with marked individuals of some of our familiar garden bumblebees have shown that they can return to the nest over distances up to 6km. It is remarkable that all of these skills are integrated and controlled by an on-board computer (brain) which is smaller than a grain of rice.

The business of being a bee

Bees capitalized on their wasp inheritance by evolving structures and behaviours which enabled them to exploit that new source of protein, pollen. The structures are:

- dense, branched hairs which trap pollen and
- specialised parts of the body where the bee compacts this pollen.

The behaviours are modified grooming movements which gather the pollen grains and concentrate them in one or two special places.

The majority of bee species transport pollen by compacting it into a dense brush of specialised hairs, the scopa. In mining bees, there is a scopa on the each of the hind legs; in the leafcutter and mason bees, the scopa is on the underside of the abdomen.

Bumblebees do not have a scopa. Instead, like their relatives, the tropical orchid bees, the stingless bees and the honeybees, they have a pollen basket or corbiculum (Plates 1 and 3). This takes the form of a slightly expanded and concave outer face of the tibia of the hind leg. Here, the bee builds up a dense mass of pollen, slightly moistened with nectar. The sides of the pollen basket are fringed with stiff, slightly curved bristles, which help to support the pollen load. In this is way, the bumblebee transports it back to the nest, where she deposits the pollen into a wax storage pot by backing over it and using her middle legs to flick the pollen mass into the pot.

As well as pollen handling structures, bees evolved longer tongues so that they could exploit nectar from deep-tubed flowers (see front cover). Some primitive groups of bee remained short-tongued, however and, like their wasp relatives, are confined to shallow, easy-access flowers.

TWO

The Colony Cycle

Spring

A bumblebee colony is founded in spring by a single queen which has emerged from hibernation. During the winter, she was sustained by the fat she laid down during the previous late summer. Now, the first really mild days have woken her up and she is ready to venture forth and find a suitable place in which to establish a nest and rear her first generation of offspring.

Newly-emerged queens are likely to be seen flying slowly up and down hedgerows, and disappearing into dense undergrowth. Here they are seeking out old mouse nests, the most popular nest sites for species such as *Bombus lucorum, B. terrestris* and *B. lapidarius*. In North America, *B. affinus* and *B. terricola* also prefer mouse nest, as does *B. lucorum,* which occurs in northern areas as well as across much of northern Eurasia.

Other species nest above ground in dense tussocks of grass or under accumulated leaf litter, such as *B. pascuorum, B. pratorum* and *B. hortorum* in Eurasia and *B. fervidus* and many other species in North America.

Both underground and surface nesters sometimes nest in cavities in drystone walls and heaps of old rubble. They will also nest in dry compost heaps and this is how bumblebee nests often first come to the attention of gardeners.

During her nest-seeking phase, the queen will feed on nectar to gain energy from this mixture of sugars. She will also eat pollen for protein, which she needs to mature the eggs in her ovaries. By dusk on her first day, if she hasn't found a suitable nest site, the queen will rest up for the night under, say, some loose bark, moss or deep in a dense clump of ivy leaves or some similar sheltered spot.

Eventually, the queen will find a nest site and, if it is an old mouse nest, she will re-arrange it, teasing the old bedding of dry grass into a ball, sometimes incorporating any dry moss which may be nearby. She makes a central cavity in this nest ball and here secretes wax from glands in her abdomen. Using her jaws and forelegs as tools, she moulds the wax into a shallow cup. This is where she first stores pollen and then lays eggs. On returning from a pollen-collecting trip, she backs over the cup and rapidly uses her middle legs to scrape off the pollen from pollen baskets on her hind legs. She then uses her jaws to tamp the pollen down into a dense mass. When sufficient pollen has been stored, she lays a batch of six to eight eggs on to the pollen. Then she secretes more wax with which she fashions a roof to seal the brood chamber.

Her next activity is reminiscent of birds, for, periodically, she sits astride her brood chamber and incubates it by generating heat. Bumblebees are able to control their body temperature and, unlike most insects, they are warm-blooded: they can generate heat chemically. The body temperature of an incubating queen is about 30°C and this is sufficient to keep her well-insulated egg clump at 30-32°C.

The heat generated by a brooding queen is sufficient to soften the wax cover and the weight of her body presses down on it, eventually forming a groove in which she sits. This ability to generate body heat also stands bumblebees in good stead during periods of cool weather, when they can forage at flowers at temperatures below which other bees are grounded.

Between bouts of incubation, the queen secretes more wax, with which she builds a thimble-sized pot for storing honey. After each foraging trip, she regurgitates nectar in the form of honey into the pot - honey is simply nectar that has had some of its water content absorbed through the lining of her honey stomach to concentrate the sugars. Bumblebees do not concentrate their honey to the same extent as honeybees, so it always remains rather more dilute and runny.

The stored honey is a valuable food: it sustains her during periods of incubation and also during bad weather when foraging at flowers is impossible.

The eggs hatch after 4-6 days and the white grub-like larvae begin to feed immediately on the stored pollen. The queen supplies them with nectar and more pollen when needed, through temporary holes she makes in the wax envelope. As the larvae grow, they moult their skins several times and the queen adds more wax to the envelope to accommodate the growing size of her brood.

Eventually, each larva spins a delicate, white cocoon made of silk produced by glands in the head and in this way creates its own cell within the larger brood chamber. Then, after 10-20 days of larval life, the larva spins a much tougher, darker cocoon. It incorporates into this faeces which have accumulated in the gut during the period of active feeding and growth.

The larva now enters the pupal stage. The pupa is the bees' equivalent of the butterfly's chrysalis and is the stage during which larval tissues are broken down and re-assembled into adult form. The adults which emerge are the first generation of workers and they appear after a pupal stage lasting about 14 days.

The timing of emergence of the first generation of workers varies with species. The earliest are usually those of *B. pratorum* (sometimes called the Early Bumblebee), which appear in late April- May, with those of *B. terrestris, B. lucorum* and *B. hortorum* appearing in May and workers of *B. pascuorum* emerging in late May-June. The precise timing, of course, depends on latitude and can also be affected by weather conditions.

Workers assist the queen in rearing subsequent generations of bees by foraging for nectar and pollen and by secreting wax for the construction of more brood chambers and food storage pots. They also defend the colony if it is attacked by predators such as rats, badgers or a range of insect enemies (See Chapter 6.)

Meanwhile, the queen is now ready to start building one or more new brood chambers which she adds to the top of the cocoons or between them. In doing so, she scrapes wax and pollen together from the top of cocoons, using this recycling to augment wax which she secretes herself. In species such as *B. pratorum* or *B. hortorum,* she lays her second batch of eggs on to a new pollen mass in the new brood chamber. In other species, the eggs are laid into wax pots without a pollen mass and the resulting larvae are fed on regurgitated pollen/honey mixtures.

Some species are sometimes referred to as "pocket-makers" because they build wax pockets or pouches near the base of the larval food chamber. Here, returning foragers deposit pollen and the larvae feed directly from this. Later on, this pollen is augmented by the queen and/or workers, which pierce temporary holes in the wax envelope, through which they squirt a regurgitated mixture of pollen and nectar.

Late spring-summer

The first generation of workers are smaller in size than later generations. This is because they rely on food collected by a single individual, the queen. Second and subsequent generations have the benefit of a larger workforce of foragers and individuals get more food during development and hence are larger. Thus the average size of workers increases with each generation.

Eventually, some larvae develop into males and queens. A single, simple factor determines if a larva is to become male: it is derived from an unfertilised egg. The queen, having mated the previous year, just before going into hibernation, stores all the sperm she is going to need in a special sac called the spermatheca. She can control the sex of an egg by using a sphincter muscle either to release or withhold sperm as the egg passes the entrance to the spermatheca on its way down the oviduct.

If the determination of males is simple, that of queens is rather more complex and not fully understood. In species such as *B. pratorum* and *B. hortorum,* it seems that larvae which become queens have had more food and have fed for longer.

Queen determination is more complex in species such as *B. terrestris, B. lucorum* and *B. lapidarius.* Here, it is thought that the queen can delay the production of new queens by using pheromones to inhibit the workers from feeding larvae as frequently or with as much food as normal, so that the larvae develop into workers. In this way, queens of such species can ensure the build up of much larger worker forces than other species.

The males eventually leave the nest and spend their time feeding at flowers.

They lack pollen baskets and so do not forage. Indeed, they rarely, if ever, return to their natal nest and spend the nights roosting in flowers or, very commonly, on thistles. Their sole rôle is to mate with young queens and this is the subject of Chapter 5.

Young queens also spend time feeding at flowers in order to build up fat to sustain them through their winter hibernation, but, unlike males, they return to their natal nests. They may forage for pollen on behalf of the colony if their mother has died.

Late summer-early autumn

Only after she is mated does a new queen leave the nest. It is then that she seeks a secure, snug place in which to hibernate. This can be in a suitable cavity under a piece of thick bark. Often, it is in a small chamber at the end of a short burrow she has excavated herself in the soil. This is usually in a north-facing bank to avoid being woken up prematurely on mild sunny days in late winter. This ploy does not always work, though. In exceptionally mild winters, queens can sometimes be seen flying in December or January. It is unlikely that such prematurely active queens will survive because they will almost certainly not have time in which to find a new place to hibernate as the temperature drops rapidly at dusk.

Meanwhile, as the emergence of the last queens is complete, the colony cycle reaches its end, with workers now mainly feeding for themselves and spending more and more time simply sitting at flowers for long periods, rather like males. Any remaining larvae eventually die of starvation and the colony dies out. Only the new generation of queens will survive to start a new cycle in the following spring.

THREE

The colony as a small business

Bees and flowers

Like us, plants reproduce sexually and pollination is their form of mating. This is the process by which pollen grains (male spores), produced in the anthers, get to the stigma, the receptive, female part of the flower. Because most species are self-sterile, this transfer of pollen is necessary: pollen must be exchanged between separate plants of the same species.

However, being literally rooted to the spot, plants need a third party to facilitate mating by proxy. Many land plants, such as grasses, pines, willows and oaks are pollinated by wind. Such plants produce billions of very light, dry pollen grains in very exposed structures such as catkins.

The majority of plants, however, have recruited insects and other animals to pollinate them, by evolving brightly coloured, conspicuous flowers which offer useful rewards in the form of energy rich nectar and an excess of protein rich pollen. In probing for nectar, the insects become dusted with pollen and, when they next visit a flower of the same species, some pollen rubs off on to the female part of the flower and pollination in accomplished.

The pollination market – how it works

The bee-flower relationship can be likened to a market-place where there is a dynamic interaction between "producer-retailers" - flowering plants - and "consumers" - pollinators, principally bees.

In our pollination market place, both the retailers and the consumers make considerable prior investments of time and energy in order to buy themselves into the market: flowering plants mobilise reserves to invest in floral structures, the synthesis of pigments, scents, nectar secretion and pollen production. And bees enter the market-place only after making time and energy investments in mating, nest-site searches and the establishment of nests. In addition to these investments, bumblebees only enter the market after investing time and energy in secreting wax and constructing the first storage cell.

Only after these prior investments can players in the market look towards making a profit. For plants, profit is measured by the number of seeds set as a result of successful pollination; for bumblebees, profit can be seen in terms of the numbers of new queens produced at the end of the colony cycle; these will go on to renew the business/colony cycle in the following spring.

As in all dynamic business situations, the players will seek to juggle the cost and benefits of their participation so as to maximise their returns and minimize their costs. Thus, plants which depend on cross-pollination are under pressure to ensure that their offered rewards, nectar, pollen and, in some cases, oils, are sufficiently abundant to attract visiting bees, but not so rich that a single visit will satiate the bee. If a bee gets all it needs from a single flower visit, then it will not visit other flowers on the same foraging trip and cross-pollination will not be effected.

Consumers, in the form of foraging bees, are under pressure to discriminate between the quality and abundance of available resources. Bees, especially the social species, are adept at assessing the sugar concentration of the nectar on offer: they can shop around and pick and choose. To help them accomplish this feat of discrimination, bees have a good visual memory and can thus return time and again to fuelling stations that offer the octane levels which best meet their immediate energetic needs. Thus they can modify their foraging behaviour according to local variations in the amount and quality of nectar available: the more nectar they find per flower visit, the more they restrict their activities to the immediate locality.

Additionally, it has recently been shown that bumblebees deposit a scent mark as they leave a flower to indicate that this particular source of nectar has been temporarily depleted. This chemical visiting card enables the bees to avoid time-wasting probing behaviour on subsequent visits.

Some flowers have evolved cunning strategies to exploit and manipulate these behavioural traits of bees. Foxglove, *Digitalis purpurea,* is a good example. This wild flower, now a popular garden species available in several colour varieties, presents its large, bell-shaped flowers in the form of a vertical inflorescence. It is pollinated exclusively by bumblebees.

Every day during the flowering season, a new flower opens at the top of the inflorescence and an old one withers at the bottom. At first, each flower is functionally male. That is, it the anthers mature and produce pollen before the female part of the flower, the stigma, becomes receptive to pollen grains and therefore capable of pollination. This means that on any given day, male flowers are at the top of the spike and females are at the bottom. Related to this is the fact that there tends to be more nectar in the lower, female flowers than in the upper, male flowers.

This way of presenting flowers and the relative timing of “maleness” and “femaleness” exploits the fact that bumblebees are optimal foragers. That is, individual bees maximise the benefit/cost ratio of their foraging by always modifying their behaviour so that they get the most nectar in the shortest time. And they do this in a quite specific way when visiting flowers which, like those of foxglove, are presented in vertical spikes. The bees have a strong tendency to visit the lower flowers first and then work their way upwards. As they do so, they face a dimin-

ishing return in terms of nectar rewards and this means that the last flowers they visit are the male ones, at the top, which are discharging pollen (Plate 2). Thus, the bees will have picked up pollen from the male flowers just when they "realize" it is time to "cut their losses" and move on to another inflorescence. When they do, they start again at the bottom of the flower spike, where the flowers are in female phase and thus pollination takes place. It is not only foxgloves which exploit this "bottom-to-top" foraging pattern of bumblebees: those other bumblebee plants *par excellence, Delphinium* and *Aconitum* spp., use exactly the same ploy.

Species of *Anchusa* have another interesting adaptation to exploit the optimal foraging behaviour of bees. Individual *Anchusa* plants may have several hundred flowers open at any one time and are able to switch nectar secretion off and on in a random, unpredictable fashion. We can liken this to a slow motion version of those Christmas tree lights which switch on an off at random.

The nectar of *Anchusa* is very rich and is produced in large quantities and is thus very attractive to high energy bees such as bumblebees. However, with the random switching on and off of nectar secretion, the bees' memory and visiting cards are of little use: they are kept guessing and it pays them therefore to probe the flowers again and again, in an immediate locality where they "know" they had a recent "fix" and find the current nectar bonanza, rather than go elsewhere. In this way, the plant manipulates the bees' nectar-seeking behaviour in order to maximise its chances of pollination.

On this basis, the pollination market is clearly a highly competitive arena and it would be naive to think of the bee-plant relationship as a simple, cosy symbiosis. It would be more accurate to regard such relationships as a complex of co-evolved necessities, forged in response to intense, competitive pressure.

By "pressure," I don't mean a conscious sense of being "driven." Rather, it is the pressure of natural selection, the driving force of evolution. At the level of the local population, there are genetically influenced variations between individual plants and bees in just how efficiently they play in the market place. On average, those individuals which have a slight edge over others will tend to leave more offspring and hence more of the "better" genes will pass into the next generation. These differences may be infinitesimally small between generations, but over the millions of years that comprise the laboratory of evolution, highly specialised combinations of structure and behaviour are selected for. This is the basis of natural selection.

Our bumblebee colony as business goes into profit if it survives long enough to produce a new generation of queens, which mate and go into hibernation and, eventually, repeat the enterprise in the following season. In getting to this state of profit, the workers of the colony will have juggled the costs and benefits of exploiting the nectar and pollen provided by the flowers. Is there not a paradox here? If profit is measured in terms of reproductive success, what is in it for the non-reproductive and apparently altruistic workers? The answer to this paradox is the subject of the next chapter.

In the meantime, it is sobering to ponder on the fact that when our pre-human ancestors left the forests of Central Africa to take up a hunter-gatherer life-style in the savannahs of East Africa, they exploited ecosystems largely made possible and maintained by networks of bee-flower relationships. True, the huge herds of grazing animals maintained the open grasslands, but the trees and flowering plants were and are largely dependent on bees as vectors of their pollen. In other words, bees and flowering plants made our humanity possible, as well as contributing to the making of each other.

FOUR

A workers life? - taking the altruism out of altruism

The selfish co-operators

Worker bumblebees are sterile females who do not usually get to lay eggs. This is despite the fact that they have ovaries. Usually, the ovaries do not develop and no eggs are formed.

In honeybees, the lack of ovarian development in workers is determined chemically by the queen: she emits a pheromone, queen substance, which suppresses the workers' ovaries. In bumblebees, it is thought that the queen uses aggression towards the workers to bring about the same result. However, as the colony grows, the queen cannot be equally aggressive to all individuals all of the time and some workers do have ovaries which develop and they lay eggs. If the queen finds a worker laying an egg, she will eat it, but she cannot hope to destroy all worker eggs, so some do survive and eventually become adult bees.

Because a worker does not mate, she has no sperm, so her eggs are unfertilised and they develop into males. Some researchers think that towards the end of a colony cycle, most males in very large colonies may be derived from worker eggs.

We have seen that the majority of workers never get to lay eggs, but spend their entire lives assisting the queen to rear more and more workers and, eventually a new generation of queens and males. We also saw that the success or profit of a colony can be measured in terms of the numbers of sexual forms which successfully mate and the number of new queens which go into hibernation and found new colonies in the following spring.

If this is so, how can workers ever be said to enjoy such a profit if they themselves do not reproduce? Is it all simply selfless altruism? If this behaviour is genetically fixed and therefore the result of natural selection, how can it be selected for if workers, by definition, have no descendents and cannot therefore pass on "altruistic" traits to subsequent generations?

To the question "Is it simply selfless altruism?" the answer is a resounding No! By giving up her own reproductive potential, a worker is, in fact being selfish. Just how this can be is directly related to the way sex is determined in wasps and bees.

Male wasps and bees are derived from unfertilised eggs, while females, including workers, are derived from fertilised eggs. It follows that a male bee receives his genetic endowment entirely from his mother: he has a grandfather, but no father and therefore has half the normal complement of genes and is said to be "haploid."

By contrast, a female bee receives half her genetic endowment from her mother, the other half from her father; she has the full set of chromosomes and is said to be "diploid."

This method of sex determination in wasps and bees distorts the genetic relationships between females in a family group. Because a male bee is haploid, all his sperm are genetically identical. A female who mates only once will therefore have a spermatheca full of genetically identical sperm and all her daughters, be they queens or workers, will receive an identical set of genes from their common father. By contrast, because the mother is diploid (has half her genes from her father, the other half from her mother), her daughters have in common only one half of the maternal genes.

We can now do a little sum to see how many genes a female bee receives from her father and how many from her mother and, immediately, we see that a female bee has a very special relationship with her sisters. On average, sisters share 75 per cent of their genes by common descent, i.e., 50 percent from the father and 25 per cent from the mother. Thus, if a female bee has a daughter, she passes on only 50 per cent of her genes into the next generation. But if she is a worker and gives up reproduction and, instead, helps her mother, the queen, to rear sisters (= the new generation of queens), more of her genes by common descent are passing into the next generation than if she had daughters of her own.

It is interesting to note that highly social behaviour has evolved 12 times in the insects, 11 of them in the order Hymenoptera, which includes the wasps, ants and bees. There must be something special about these insects and it is, of course, their unique method of sex determination, haplo-diploidy, in which males are derived from un-fertilised eggs. As we have seen, in terms of the numbers of genes she passes into the next generation, it pays a worker to forgo having daughters of her own and help rear sisters instead. This peculiar form of natural selection is called kin selection. And it takes the altruism out of altruism.

FIVE

The mating game

The male of the species

Male bumblebees have one aim in life: to mate with as many queens as possible. Once they have emerged from their natal cells, male bumblebees leave the nest and rarely return. They lack pollen baskets and so could not, in any case, collect pollen They spend all of their nights in or on flowers and most of the day alternating between gorging themselves on nectar (Plate 4) and seeking mates. However, research on some North American species has shown that before they leave the nest, the males of four species, *B. affinis, B. bimaculatus, B. griseocollis* and *B. pennsylvanicus,* incubate brood cells just like queens and workers and it is possible that this paternal care may be found in other species also.

Because queens usually mate only once, as the season progresses, males are faced with a diminishing resource in the form of virgins. For this reason, they have devised a number of strategies to maximise the number of encounters with potential mates.

The males of some species are aggressively territorial. They adopt some prominent vantage point, such as an isolated rock or protruding twig and chase away other males and any other insects which arrive in the vicinity. They also leave the perches to chase after queens that come close by. This behaviour has been described for an Asian species, *B. rufofasciatus* and a North American bumblebee, *B. nevadensis.* The males of both species have greatly enlarged eyes, which enable them to react rapidly to movement and chase potential mates.

Most male bumblebees adopt another strategy. They patrol regular beats or circuits and deposit scent droplets at various place along the route. Several males may use the same circuit and the same scent-marking spots; because they are spread out, direct competition between them is rare.

In Britain and Europe, circuits are usually between 100m and 1000m long, with up to 30 males flying along it at any one time. One study in South America showed that between 460 and 720 males of *B. pullatus* patrolled a circuit that was 2.5km long (approx. 1.5 miles).

When they are scent marking, male bumblebees alight at a plant stem, often grass, and run up and down it, rapidly opening and closing their mandibles, releasing scent from glands at the mandibular base. The males have a dense brush of hairs on the outside of each mandible, a sort of moustache, which acts as a paintbrush and is used to disperse the scent along the surface they are marking.

The males of several species may have circuits in the same locality and overlap with each other. This does not lead to confusion, however, because the scent produced by each bumblebee is a species-specific blend of volatiles. The scent is easily detectable by humans. Take a male bumblebee gently between finger and thumb and have a good sniff: most species have a distinctly lemony smell, with other overtones – males do not have a sting: you can tell them from queens and workers by their longer antennae and the fact that they have a distinct patch of dense, pale hairs on the front of the head.

Apart from distinctive scents, male bumblebees have another way of recognising themselves and making themselves recognizable to their own queens: each species tends to have its circuit at different heights above the ground. For example, the circuits of *B. terrestris* and *B. hortorum* are less than 1m above the ground, and those of *B. lucorum* are between 5 and 10m high. Males of *B. lapidarius* patrol at up to 17m above the ground. The high fliers deposit their scent on the leaf stalks of trees and tall shrubs.

The scent spots along the circuit have an arrestant effect on any virgin queens who come near, that is, the scent induces them to alight on the ground or a leaf. When the next male of the same species comes along the circuit, he will attempt to mate with her. Males rarely detect queens which are more than 40cm from a scent-marked spot.

The mating circuits of bumblebees usually do not include many flowers. The males thus fuel their patrolling flights by drinking nectar at flowers away from the circuit. It is very common to find males and young females feeding at the same flowers, with no attempts at mating being made (Plate 5). Flowers are for feeding, circuits are for mating: context is everything.

SIX

Enemies and nest associates

Predators

Perhaps because of their stings, bumblebees have few predators. In the British Isles, rats, mice and badgers sometimes destroy nests while eating the stored, sweet honey and larvae; in North America, skunks are frequent destroyers of bumblebee nests and seem not to be deterred by being stung.

In Greenland, one of the worst enemies of bumblebees are mink and the bee larvae are an important part of their diet.

Bird predators include Spotted Flycatchers, which deal with the bee's sting by rubbing the insect along a branch and immobilising it. Red-backed Shrikes, sometimes called Butcher Birds, catch bumblebees and impale them, together with other prey items, on thorns. In Mediterranean areas, Bee-eaters remove the stings before eating their prey.

Many bumblebees fall prey to spiders by being caught in their webs. They are also eaten by crab spiders, e.g. *Misumetia vatia,* which do not make webs, but instead lurk motionless on flowers and pounce while the bee is busy feeding. The spiders escape detection by matching the colour of the flower on which they are sitting (Plate 6).

Parasitic Worms

A parasitic nematode worm, *Sphaerulia bombi,* is one of the most specialised enemies of bumblebees. It lives exclusively inside the bodies of queen bumblebees in Europe and North America. The bees become infected while they hibernate in the soil over winter. During this time, a mated adult female of the worm burrows into the body of the queen. When the queen emerges the following spring, the presence of the worm has had profound effects on the bee's physiology and behaviour. It prevents the release of a hormone which triggers the development of the queen's ovaries and somehow shuts down the nesting instinct of the bee. Instead, she forages only for herself, living among flowers, where she moves around in a rather haphazard, desultory manner.

During this time, the worm's reproductive system literally turns itself inside-out and is 10-20mm long, with the rest of the worm in the form of a tiny head attached to this. Eventually, hundreds of the worm's eggs are shed into the bee's blood system and these develop into tiny larvae 1mm long. These migrate to the bee's gut and are shed with the faeces.

Somehow, the presence of the worm induces the queen to return to her hibernation site, where she may be joined by other infected queens. They shed larvae into the soil, which will infect other queens when they hibernate in the same site. In this way the worm ensures that it spreads into the next generation of queens.

Mites

Mites are tiny relatives of spiders and many species are associated in one way or another with bees. Queen bumblebees in early spring are often seen carrying a load of mites, *Parasitellus fucorum*, from flower to flower (Plate 7). The mites accompanied the queen when she left her nest to find a place in which to hibernate and they spent the winter buried deep in her fur. Now they are seeking to remain with her until she founds a nest and here they will scavenge on food debris and bee droppings and possibly on stored pollen.

Not all of the mites will hang on to the queen: some will drop off and lurk on flowers until another bumblebee comes along and they will hitch a ride to a new colony in this way.

Flies

A number of flies are adapted to undergo their development in the nests of bumblebees, the two commonest being *Fannia canicularis* and *Volucella bombylans*. *Fannia* is related to the housefly and its larvae have a scavenging function among the cells of *Bombus* nests, feeding on wax and pollen debris and larval faeces.

Adults of the hoverfly, *Volucella bombylans,* are very effective mimics of bumblebees (Plate 8). The fly exists in different colour forms, each mimicking different species of *Bombus.* Thus there is one which mimics white-tailed species and another which mimics red-tailed species.

The mimicry does not end there: these flies, if attacked, adopt the same threat posture as their bumblebee models, that is, they lay on one side, raise their exposed middle leg in the air and make a loud, distinctive buzz.

The females of *Volucella bombylans* enter the nests of bumblebees to lay their eggs. They have a superb adaptation if they are attacked and killed by defending workers: as they die, a reflex action eliminates eggs from the body, so the female fly is able to reproduce.

The eggs have a very sticky surface which helps them to adhere to the substrate and it may also protect them from the bees.

Two of the cone-headed flies, *Conops vesicularis* and *Physocephala rufipes,* have larvae specifically adapted to feed on the tissues inside the abdomens of bumblebees. In North America, there are four species of *Physocepha* associated with bumblebees, *P. burgessi, P.marginata, P. sagittaria* and *P. texana.*

The female flies each have a specialized, dagger-like ovipositor or egg-laying tube. They lie in wait for bumblebees at flowers and use this to inject an egg directly into the abdomen of a visiting bumblebee. Here, the egg hatches and the larva feeds slowly on the tissues, eventually killing the bee. The horny cuticle of the bee's abdomen acts as protection for the pupating fly, which remains inside until the new adult fly emerges following spring.

Cuckoo bumblebees

As the name implies, these bees are cuckoos in the nests of bumblebees, in just the same sense as the cuckoo birds. These cuckoos are very closely related to their hosts and are in fact placed in *Psithyrus,* subgenus of *Bombus*.

There are six species of *Psithyrus* in the British Isles, and North America also has six, but the two faunas do not share any species. All have in common the absence of a worker caste, the females lack pollen baskets or corbiculae and they have a very thick cuticle. This last feature is supposed to help protect the cuckoos against the defending stings of host colonies. It does not always work, though: strong nest populations of *Bombus terrestris* and *B. lucorum* are often littered with the corpses of invading females of *Psithyrus* which have failed to run the gauntlet of defending workers.

The females of some species of *Psithyrus* closely resemble their host queens in appearance. Thus *P. rupestris* is, like its host, *Bombus lapidarius,* all black in colour, with a bright red tail.

When a female *Psithyrus* enters a nest, she will try to burrow down into the nest material and stay there many hours. During this time, she is absorbing the scent of the nest and, when she emerges to mingle with her host workers, she is unrecognised as a dangerous interloper: smelling of the correct scent is the passport to social acceptance in bumblebee society.

In colonies where the *Bombus* host queen survives and continues to lay eggs, the *Psithyrus* queen follows her around and eats the eggs she lays before laying her own eggs (Plate 9). I have observed this on a number of occasions and wondered how the *Psithyrus* queen distinguishes between her own eggs and those of her host queen.

Close observation in a nest of *Bombus lucorum* which hosted a female of *Psithyrus polemics* revealed that before eating an egg, the *Psithyrus* female feels it all over with the tip of her tongue. I took samples of *Psithyrus* and *Bombus* eggs and compared them under the microscope. The eggs of *Bombus* where, like the eggs of most bees, pearly and smooth. Those of *Psithyrus,* however, had a dense pattern of reticulations over the entire surface. Presumably this stark difference in surface texture enables the cuckoo female to distinguish between her own eggs and those of the host species.

Cuckoo bumblebees don't always get things their own way, though. They are just as susceptible to parasitisation by the nematode worm mentioned earlier, *Sphaerulia bombi.*

SEVEN

Frequently asked questions

1. **Do bumblebees die after stinging?**
No, a bumblebee lives to sting another day. It is only honeybee workers which die after stinging. This is because the sting bears short, backwardly directed teeth which engage in the skin of the victim. As the bee struggles to free herself, the sting and venom gland remain in the wound, pumping venom. At the same time, small glands attached to the sting apparatus emit an alarm pheromone, a special scent which recruits other workers of the same colony to attack. In this way, honeybees can mount a level of co-ordinated defence which is not available to bumblebees.

2. **Do male bumblebees die after mating?**
No, male bumblebees can mate many times. It is the male (drone) honeybee which dies after mating, because his genitalia become detached and remain inside the queen.

3. **According to the laws of aerodynamics, bumblebees shouldn't be able to fly, so how do they do it?**
Bumblebees clearly can fly, so either the laws of aerodynamics are wrong or our understanding of them is suspect. There *is* a problem, however, so long as we think of bumblebees as fixed-wing aircraft: the surface area of the wings relative to the volume and mass of the body would *not* be capable of lifting the bees off the ground. However, bumblebees are not fixed-wing air craft: they are helicopters. Each of the two hind wings couples to the fore wings by means of a row of tiny hooks or *hamuli,* which engage with the trailing edge of the forewings. This creates a functional, hinged unit which is very flexible along its longitudinal axis: the wing-tips describe a figure of eight pattern as the wings beat and this creates vortices along the length of the wings which create more than enough lift to facilitate flight. The laws of aerodynamics are thus not compromised and flight engineers can sleep again at night.

4. **Do bumblebees make honey?**
Yes, but they do not ripen it in the way that honeybees do, so it remains less concentrated, more watery and therefore liable to fermentation. Because bumblebees, unlike honeybees, have annual rather than perennial colonies, they do not have to store large amounts of honey. Thus bumblebee honey

would never be a commercially viable product. By contrast, honeybee colonies need a large honey store because the whole colony survives the winter and needs an energy rich food to see them through this annual lean period, when foraging is impossible. In bumblebees, only the new generation of queens survives the winter in hibernation. Before going into hibernation, the queens feed voraciously and build up a store of fat which on which they subsist.

5. **Do bumblebees swarm?**

No, only honeybees swarm. It is a strategy for dividing large, populous colonies. An old queen leaves the hive with a large number of workers in a "swarm." They settle close to the hive in a cluster – often on the branch of a tree – while scout workers seek out a new nest site. When they return, they communicate the distance and direction of the new nest site by means of the famous dance language, by which they normally communicate information about food resources. The swarm then flies off *en masse* to the new nest site.

EIGHT

Bumblebees as managed pollinators of crops

Pollination and political economy

It has been calculated that the pollination services of honeybees are worth at least 50 times the total value of the annual world honey crop. This gives some idea of just how valuable bees are to human economies.

Bumblebees, too, figure prominently in the balance sheet of human affairs. The 19th century German biologists, Ernst Haeckel and Karl Vogt, jokingly referred to this when they suggested that the might of the British Empire depended on bumblebees. Their reasoning was that the Empire's power depended to a great extent on the Royal Navy, which was fed on beef from cattle fed on red clover (*Trifolium pratense*), which was pollinated by bumblebees.

While possibly facetious at the time, Haeckel and Vogt could hardly have guessed just how prophetic their suggestion was, for there is no doubt that in the late 1940's and 1950's, Britain's post-war recovery depended to some considerable extent on the pollination services of bumblebees. Just how this came about is a fascinating story.

The early European colonists in New Zealand found themselves in an environment that was ideal for rearing sheep and cattle. The climate and soils were also suitable for growing red clover, an important forage crop for cattle. Clovers are important for another reason: being leguminous plants, they add to soil fertility via the activities of nitrogen-fixing bacteria which live symbiotically in their roots. In other words, pastures sown with clover do not need the addition of artificial, nitrogenous fertilizers.

On the face of it, then, those early cattle and sheep ranchers were in a win-win situation. But things were not so simple: the few bee species native to New Zealand all belong to relatively primitive, short-tongued groups of bees which are incapable of pollinating the deep-tubed flowers of red clover. Even the tongues of honeybees are not long enough. As a result, pollination of clover was insufficient to produce adequate seed set and the potential profits of the cattle ranchers were not fully realised: New Zealand became a net annual importer of clover seed.

Then, in the 1890's someone had the bright idea of importing four long-tongued species of bumblebee from Britain: *Bombus lapidarius, B. hortorum, B. ruderatus* and *B. subterraneus.* The bees adapted well to their new surroundings, became established and their economic impact can be judged by the fact that within five years, New Zealand became a net exporter rather than an importer of clover seed.

And how did this affect Britain's post-war recovery? It gave access to cheap meat and dairy products. The effects were not all economic. There were political implications as well because General de Gaulle's long-standing opposition to British entry into the European Common Market was based on what he and his European colleagues saw as Britain's unfair economic advantage, conferred by access to this cheap antipodean produce.

There is an irony in the New Zealand bumblebee story. One of the species involved, *Bombus ruderatus,* is now very rare in the UK and another, *B. subterraneus,* is now almost certainly extinct here (see Chapter 9). Both species continue to thrive in New Zealand and contribute to the agricultural wealth of the country. The continuing success story of bumblebees in New Zealand is based on populations which became established in the wild.

Commercial use of bumblebees

The most recent success stories involve the commercial propagation of colonies in artificial nests in Britain and Europe and their sale to growers of glasshouse fruit and vegetables.

Next time you are in your local supermarket buying out of season strawberries, courgettes, tomatoes, aubergines and sweet peppers, you can thank commercially reared bumblebees for making this possible. A native bee, *Bombus terrestris,* is the species used in this way.

Colonies of *B. terrestris* take particularly well to artificial nests and can build up to 3-500 workers. They are relatively easy to rear in large, economically viable quantities. Unlike honeybees, which most of their time and energy trying to escape, they thrive in glasshouses and poly-tunnels.

The seasonal activity cycles of *B. terrestris* can be manipulated to suit the needs of growers. This is fortunate because, in Britain and northern and central Europe, the horticultural growing season begins in March, when *B. terrestris* queens are just beginning to emerge and seek nest sites and well before colonies have reached a useful size for pollination purposes. Likewise, in Mediterranean countries, glasshouse crops need to be pollinated from autumn onwards, just when colonies are going into decline and the new generation of queens is going into hibernation.

Research has shown that queens of *B. terrestris* can be induced to enter a six-month hibernation period by exposing them to appropriate doses of carbon dioxide gas (CO_2). Thus they can be revived to establish new colonies to have foraging and therefore pollinating workers just when the growers need them. This means that the colonies must be established 15-20 weeks before the main flowering period of the target crops.

There is another reason why bumblebees score over honeybees in terms of pollinating efficiency. Tomatoes, aubergines and peppers present their pollen in an unusual way: instead of ripe pollen grains dusting the outer surfaces of the anthers, these plants shed their pollen into a chamber inside the anther and the grains gain access to the outside world via a single pore at the apex of the anther.

Such plants are adapted for pollination by bees which are capable of what is called "buzz pollination." This involves the bee clinging on to the anthers and vibrating its wing muscles at a very high frequency. These vibrations liberate the pollen grains via the pore and the bee becomes dusted with them. The activity is accompanied by a high-pitched buzzing, hence the name "buzz pollination." This behaviour is not part of the honeybee's repertoire, so they are not the pollinators of choice for these crops.

Tomatoes, aubergines and peppers do not occur naturally within the range of *Bombus terrestris,* so just how the workers of this bee "know" that a particular crop needs buzz pollination remains a mystery.

Apart from colonies actively managed for pollination in glasshouses and poly-tunnels, wild populations of bumblebees play a vital role in the pollination of forage crops such as clovers (*Trifolium* spp.) and sainfoin (*Onobrychis sativa),* broad beans/field beans (*Vicia faba*), and oil seeds such as rape *(Brassica napus*), white mustard (*Sinapis alba*) and flax/linseed (*Linum usitatissimum*). For this reason, the conservation of bumblebees should be high on the agendas of all those bodies concerned with the conservation of habitats and the rational management of agricultural landscapes (Chapter 9).

NINE

Encouraging bumblebees in your garden

Growing the right mix of plants

The easiest way to attract bumblebees to your garden is to grow plants that they particularly like. Avoid double-flowered varieties. Such plants have been bred artificially to have the male and female parts of the flower replaced by extra whorls of petals. Often the nectaries are lost too or greatly reduced, so that the flowers are of no interest to bees.

Bumblebees are long-tongued bees and like tubular flowers, though they will readily visit willow catkins. They are particularly fond of:-

Comfrey, *Symphytum spp.*: shorter tongued species of *Bombus* will bite a hole at the base of the flower, so by-passing the sexual parts, thus effectively robbing the flower, without contributing to pollination.
Yellow Archangel, *Galeobdolon luteum.*
White Deadnettle, *Lamium album.*
Red Deadnettle, *L. purpureum.*
Sages, *Salvia* spp.
Thymes, *Thymus* spp.
Marjoram, *Origanum vulgare.*
Rosemary, *Rosmarinum officinale.*
Lavenders, *Lavandula* spp.
Lamb's Ears, *Stachys lanata.*
Skullcaps, *Scutellaria* spp.
Bugles, *Ajuga* spp.
Geraniums, *Geranium* spp.
Snapdragons, *Anthirrinum* spp.
Toadflaxes, *Linum* spp.
Sweet peas, *Lathyrus* spp.
Buddleia, *Buddleja davidii*
Foxglove, *Digitalis purpurea.*
Purple Toadflax, *Linaria purpurea.*

Many garden centres now sell seed mixtures of old meadow plants such as Bird's Foot Trefoil, *Lotus corniculatus,* clovers, *Trifolium* spp. and poppies, *Papaver* sp. All of these are attractive to bumblebees.

Gardeners who grow broad beans, *Vicia faba,* will find bumblebees useful pollinators. They also pollinate raspberries, strawberries and blackcurrants.

For detailed information on managing a garden for wildlife, including bees, see J. Steel's book listed in Further Reading.

Keeping bumblebees in artificial nests

The following account gives guidelines to the use and management of bumblebee nest boxes supplied by the Oxford Bee Company Ltd. (Plate 12). It is suitable for common garden bumblebees in Britain, Europe and North America.

Before you site you nest: ensure that the bottom of both the inner and outer chambers is lined with the piece of corrugated cardboard provided. This is to absorb any excess moisture produced by the bees when the colony is at full size. Then place the provided fibrous nesting material on top of this bottom lining.

In the outer chamber, fill the feeding cup with dilute honey or syrup solution – dilute one tablespoon of honey/syrup in two tablespoons of water.

Siting your nest:

In early spring, find a sheltered, shady, south-facing spot. Under a dense evergreen shrub is fine, as is the base of a dense hedge if your garden has one. Avoid situations where the nest will ever be in direct sunlight. You could also try placing your nest in a cavity in the side of a relatively dry part of a compost heap that you wouldn't mind devoting to bees. Ensure that the gauze-covered ventilation holes are not blocked.

To make the entrance seem more natural to the bees, heap some dry grass or old plant stems around it, ensuring that there is a free passage into the hole. Place a landmark such as a white stone close to the entrance passage in the clump of dry grass.

You can also site occupied nests in an unheated greenhouse or garden shed if you are interested in making regular observations of your bees.

Wherever you site your nest out of doors, ensure that it is raised above the soil by placing it on four stones or pieces of brick.

This should now be attractive to nest-seeking queens recently emerged from hibernation. However, as with bird nest boxes, there are no guarantees that your nest will be used in any given year. But, unlike bird nest boxes, you *can* take active steps to get a queen to nest by catching a one and introducing her to the nest.

Finding, catching your queen and setting her up – when, where and how?

When: the first queen bumblebees wake from hibernation in early spring. Exactly when this is will depend on where you live. In southern Britain and southern central Europe, queens of some large species will appear as early as mild days in February. These first appearances will take place later and later, the further north you go. Apart from geographical considerations, there is variation between species: some start earlier than others, with the queens of a few species not emerging until late April-early May. However, most will make their first appearances from mid-March, through April.

Where to look: the easiest bumblebees to domesticate are those species which normally nest in old, abandoned mouse nests, so the best places in which to find nest-seeking queens are where field mice are likely to nest: along old, deep, dense hedgerows and woodland edge.

Nest-seeking queens have a very characteristic flight pattern: they fly slowly and close to the ground in a rather “bumbling” fashion, often landing and disappearing for a short while into the undergrowth. In gardens, they can be seen bumbling their way among early flowers.

A good way of finding nest-seeking queens is to visit some old hedgerows on a warm spring day and stand in, say, a gap in the hedge or in a gateway. You can then use the literal edges of both sides of the hedge as a sight line along which to look. A pair of binoculars might help. Additionally, you can walk and search along the irregular edges of some woodland. Always seek the permission of landowners before doing this.

In gardens, queens may be seen loitering around old compost heaps, using the characteristic “bumbling” flight pattern mentioned above. Alternatively, you may find some visiting early flowers – daffodils, snowdrops, willow catkins.

Queens to avoid: any which are collecting pollen. This is because a pollen-laden queen has already found and established a nest and may even have some early offspring. You want to collect a queen which is clearly *still in nest-seeking mode.* There should be no difficulty in finding queens in early spring, not least because, being queens, they are much larger and more conspicuous than the more familiar workers, which often forage in large numbers in well-stocked gardens later in the year.

How to catch and handle your queens:
You will need:-

- A net with which to catch your bees. If you don’t have a net available, then find look for some feeding at flowers and catch them in the jars/ canisters described below.
- Some clean, screw-top glass jars, each lined with some kitchen towel,

or, some 35mm film canisters in which to put your captive queen(s). The kitchen towel is to give the bee something on which to gain purchase with its clawed feet and to absorb any moisture the bee may produce. Punch ventilation holes into the lids of the jars/film canisters.

A cold box and some ice packs (if you are going to catch bees away from your home garden).

When you have caught a queen, swing the net around rapidly so the bee is at the far end. Then, with a glass jar/film canister in one hand and the lid in the other, quickly place you hand with the jar into the net and enclose the bee in the jar, making sure that the neck of the jar is sealed by the net so that the bee cannot escape. Then, insert your hand which is holding the lid into the net and – you now have both hands in the top of the net - quickly apply the lid. If you are not used to catching insects in this way, it is a good idea to practice these moves without any target insect until they become second nature.

Although the bee, when captive in the net, will make a loud, protesting buzz, you are unlikely to get stung so long as you don't actually grasp it in your hand. *However, if you have a history of allergic reaction to insect stings, then avoid this procedure altogether. Either get a friend who is not so affected to help you or simply place your nest in the garden as described above and rely on a nest-seeking queen to find it for herself.*

Now place your bee in the cold box for the journey home. This will calm her down and minimize the chance of her regurgitating the contents of the honey-stomach and soiling herself. If you are catching bees in your home garden, you can put the jar/canister containing you bee straight in the fridge: it is a good idea to have her chilled and therefore immobile and docile when placing her in the nest.

Having placed your nest in a suitable site (see above) and put your feeding cup with honey/syrup solution in the outer chamber, you are now ready to put your chilled bee into her nest. Place her in the outer chamber, taking care to ensure she does not come into contact with the liquid food. Now block the nest entrance with a cork or other suitable bung – a dense wedge of kitchen towel should be suitable, but a cork or rubber bung cut to size with a knife is best. Confine your bee in this way for 2 days. The idea is that she will get used to her new surroundings and adopt them as "home." She will feed on the honey/syrup solution. After 2 days, remove the bung; if the queen has taken to her nest, she will eventually emerge and make some orientation flights so as to memorize both near and distant landmarks and then get down to the business of building wax cells in which to store pollen and lay eggs.

Additional steps you can take to increase nesting success:-

1. Put your nest in an unheated greenhouse or garden shed. Place jars of cut flowers around the place. White Deadnettle and Comfrey are best, but daffodils will do. Introduce your bee(s) into the building. In the case of a garden shed with distinct windows, it might be a good idea to cover the window(s) with some cotton gauze or old net curtains to prevent the bees from concentrating on trying to get out via the windows. They will eventually find the flowers for food and the nest. Once they have taken up residence and established a nest (indicated by the queen returning to the nest with pollen compacted into the pollen baskets on her hind legs), you can think about putting the nest out in the garden. Do this at dusk, when the bee(s) will be back in the nest (See below under "If you have to re-site an occupied nest).

2. Try confining two queens for two days. Some researchers have found that if two queens are confined together in this way, then this increases the chances of one taking up permanent residence and successfully founding a colony. With two queens so-confined, a dominance hierarchy is established, with one, usually the largest, becoming dominant, with the subservient one helping with the labour of secreting wax for cell construction and foraging for pollen and nectar. Often the dominance hierarchy results in fighting, with the dominant queen killing the subservient one. Whatever happens, the theory is that the bee which has fought to establish herself as the dominant individual has made such a large investment in terms of time and energy that she feels "possessive" about her newly-acquired nest and is reluctant to abandon it. Apparently, it doesn't matter if the two confined queens belong to different species.

If you need to re-site an occupied nest: do this at dusk or after dark, when the bees are all back at the nest. Block the nest entrance with tissue paper and, very gently, lift the nest and take it to your new site. You will hear some angry buzzing from inside, but do not be alarmed.

If the new site is not too far from the original one, then the bees will have no difficulty in re-learning a slightly different set of landmarks. If, however, you need to move it for more than a few metres, then it is best to do this in short stages, moving the nest a sort distance one night and then leaving it for two days and then moving it again at dusk and so on.

Looking inside your nest: under the lid there is a transparent plastic roof, which enables you to see what is going on inside the nest without the bees escaping. It is best to make inspections early in the morning or at dusk so as to minimize disturbance to the bees. When removing and replacing the lid, always do so with slow, gentle movements.

Caring for and cleaning your nest: Once the queen has established herself in the nest, there is no need to keep the feeder cup in place and this can be removed one evening when the queen is at rest. The Oxford Bee Co bumblebee nest is a low maintenance affair. If you have an occupied nest, all you need to do is to replace at intervals the corrugated cardboard liner in the outer (smaller) chamber with a fresh piece or double or triple layer of paper towel. Do this at dusk when the bees are inactive.

If your nest has been occupied, it will need cleaning in late autumn, when the colony has died out and the new generation of queens has left to seek places in which to hibernate. First, remove the nest material, which is upholsterer's kapok. Keep a little of this back to add to a new batch for next year's nesting: the smell of used nest material will make the nest attractive to nest-seeking queens in the following spring. Now remove the corrugated cardboard floor covering. If this is not damp or not too soiled, it can be used the following spring. Again, the scent of used nest material might attract queens. Use a vacuum cleaner to remove debris and then store it in a dry place. Initially, it might be a good idea to store it behind a radiator to give it a good drying out. If the floor lining is very soiled and/or damp, discard it and replace it with a new piece of corrugated cardboard next spring.

Now wash the inside of the nest with very hot soapy water. DO NOT USE BLEACH OR DISINFECTANT – THE RESIDUAL SMELL OF THESE LIQUIDS MAY DETER NEST-SEEKING QUEENS IN THE FOLLOWING SPRING.

New upholsterer's kapok can be bought from sowing and craft stores. NEVER use cotton wool, the strands of which catch on the bees, clawed feet, trapping them.

The species you can expect: the big six

Bombus terrestris **– Buff-tailed bumblebee** (Plate 1)
One of the most widespread and common species in Britain, Eire and Europe, this is the species now managed commercially for the pollination of various greenhouse crops (See Chapter 8).
Identification: queens, workers and males with dark yellow band at front of thorax and base of abdomen, tail buff-coloured in British populations, white in continental Europe and therefore difficult to distinguish there from the next species.

***Bombus lucorum* – Common White-tailed bumblebee** (Plate 10)
Also widespread and common in Britain, Eire and much of Europe. Found also in Northern USA and Canada.
Identification: queens and workers with bright lemon yellow band at front of thorax and base of abdomen, tail white. Males with pale yellow hairs on front and top of head and much of front half of thorax and forming a band at the base of the abdomen; tail white. Much shaggier in appearance than the shorter-haired *B. terrestris.*

***Bombus lapidarius* – Common Red-tailed bumblebee**
Common and widespread in much of lowland Britain, Eire and Europe.
Identification: queens and workers entirely black with a bright, orange red tail. (Easily confused with the smaller and rarer *B. ruderarius,* which differs in the queen and worker in having reddish rather than black hairs fringing the upper side of the pollen basket); males with yellow hairs on hear and front of thorax.

***Bombus pratorum* – Early bumblebee** (Plate 5)
Common and widespread in Britain, Eire and Europe.
Identification: the commonest of the small, red-tailed species; queens and workers with pale yellow hairs forming a band at the front and rear of the thorax, the bands separated by black; base of abdomen with yellow band, tail red; males with considerable and variable amounts of yellow on head, thorax, base of abdomen; tail black.

***Bombus pascuorum* – Common Pasture bumblebee** (Plate 11)
Common and widespread in Britain, Eire and Europe.
Identification: the commonest of the "ginger" species; queens, workers and males entirely covered with gingery hairs, with variable admixture of black hairs, the latter often forming indistinct bands on the abdomen.

***Bombus hortorum* – Common Garden bumblebee** (Front cover)
Common and widespread in Britain, Eire and Europe.
Identification: the commonest very long-tongued species- average tongue length 13.5mm, with a very elongate face; queens, workers and males with pale yellow hair bands at front and rear of thorax and base of abdomen, with white tail; males additionally with pale hairs on the head.

TEN

Why we need to conserve our wild bees

The present situation

In Britain, 25% of our 254 bee species are now on the *Red Data Book* list of endangered species. This includes five species of bumblebee which, 20 years ago, where widespread and common. These included *Bombus ruderatus* and *B. sylvarum,* which are now very rare and restricted in their distribution. One species, *B. subterraneus,* is almost certainly extinct in the UK. In parts of Central Europe the situation is worse, with nearly 45% listed in the *Red Data Book.*

The reasons for decline

The large scale intensification of British agriculture that took place in the 1970's and 1980's resulted in a steady reduction if floral diversity and nesting habitat. This included the steady erosion of traditional hay-making practices with a consequent loss of floral diversity, especially among long-tubed flowers associated with hay meadows, such as Bird's Foot Trefoil, *Lotus corniculatus,* several species of melilots and medicks, *Melilotus* spp. and *Medicago* spp. Also popular were Red Bartsia, *Odontites verna* and Yellow Rattle, *Rhinanthus minor.* These two plants are parasites on the roots of other meadow flowers and their presence is an indicator of the health and diversity of plant habitats associated with traditionally maintained hay-making.

These species are particularly attractive to the longer-tongued species of bumblebee which have been hardest hit by modern agriculture, species such as *Bombus ruderatus, B. ruderarius, B. sylvarum, B. humilis, B. muscorum* and *B. subterraneus.*

Another factor in the decline of our bumblebee populations is the loss of hedgerows – 160,000km in the UK since 1945. This has come about under pressure to accommodate larger and larger farm machinery, with increasing turning circles. The loss of hedgerows is serious because it represents loss of nesting habitats for many species, especially those which secondarily use mouse nests. Associated with the loss of hedgerows is another loss of floral diversity.

Even hedgerows which survive modern agriculture are often abused. The habit of tidying up hedgerows with severe trimmings once or twice a year also contributes to the loss of diversity. Moreover, hedgerows are excellent mimics in structural and floral terms of woodland edge, another habitat which is on the decline and yet another reason for paying attention to the state of our hedgerows.

This is not supposed to be an attack on beleaguered farmers. Rather, it is a call to recognize that if we want farmers to exercise stewardship over the countryside on our behalf, then we will have to make it worth their while in financial terms.

Meanwhile, there are six species of *Bombus* and five species of *Psithyrus* which continue to flourish in urban and suburban gardens. This is because of the contrived diversity of flowering plants found in domestic habitats, together with plenty of nesting opportunities.

It is possible to add to these nesting opportunities with the help of nests available from the Oxford Bee Co Ltd (See next section).

Where to get your bumblebee nests

Bumblebee nest kits, complete with full instructions, are available from Oxford Bee Company Ltd:

Oxford Bee Company Ltd.,
Ark Business Centre,
Gordon Road,
Loughborough,
LEICS LE11 1JP

Tel: 01509 261654
Fax: 01509 643465
E-mail: info@oxbeeco.com
Website: http://www.oxbeeco.com

Oxford Bee Company Ltd also supplies nest kits for the Red Mason Bee, *Osmia rufa,* the European Horned Mason Bee, *Osmia* cornuta and the European Blue Mason Bee, *Osmia coerulescens,* as well as ladybird houses, which provide roosting and hibernation sites for these useful predators of aphids.

For information leaflets and a complete price list of products supplied by Oxford Bee Company Ltd and a list of publications distributed by the OBC, please contact the above.

Further reading and useful websites

Alford, D. V. 1975. *Bumblebees.* Davis-Poynter, London, 352pp.

[A very comprehensive account of bumblebee biology; now out of print, but available in libraries.]

Benton, E. 2000. *The Bumblebees of Essex.* Lopinga Books, Wimbish Books. 180pp.

[An excellent guide to the identification and natural history of bumblebees. Although confined in scope to the English county of Essex, it offers a very user-friendly way to identify all the common bumblebee species to be found in gardens. Well illustrated with high quality colour photographs.]

Buchmann, S. L. & Nabhan, G. P. 1997. *The Forgotten Pollinators.* Shearwater Books, California. 320pp.

[An excellent and highly readable account of how we depend, for 80 per cent of our food, on the unmanaged pollination services of wild bees and other insects, and just how much the life-sustaining relationships between bees and plants are threatened by human degradation of habitats.]

Delaplane, K., S. & Mayer, D. E. 2000. *Crop Pollination by Bees.* (CABI, Wallingford, 344pp.

[A comprehensive overview of bees as managed crop pollinators in temper ate regions.]

Free, J.B. & Butler, C. G. 1959. *Bumblebees.* Collins New Naruralist, London, 208pp.

[A comprehensive account of British bumblebees. Out of print but available in most libraries.]

Heinrich, B. 1979. *Bumblebee Economics.* Harvard University Press, Massachusetts and London. 245pp.

[This book is so clearly and beautifully written, it is a classic example of how a technical work can be accessible to the non-specialist layman. Apart from a general treatise on bumblebee natural history, this book deals with their ener getics in relation to pollination and how to rear them in artificial nests. Heinrich also shows how the economic theories of Adam Smith, while not now thought to be applicable to human societies, seem to work rather well for bumblebee colonies.]

Matheson, A. (Editor). 1996. *Bumblebees for Pleasure and Profit.* International Bee Research Assocition, Cardiff. 47pp.

[Based on presentations given at a symposium organised by the International Bee Research Association, this book deals with bumblebees as pollinators of native floras and as managed pollinators of crops, as well as their domestica tion and educational potential in schools.]

O'Toole, C. 1995. *Alien Empire: an Exploration of the Lives of Insects.* (BBC Books, London. 224pp.

[The book of the BBCtv series of the same name, this is a detailed account of the ecological importance of insects for the rest of life on Earth.]

O'Toole, C. & Raw, A. 1994. *Bees of the World.* Blandford-Cassell, London. 192pp.

[A comprehensive and highly illustrated account of the fascinating natural histories of bees from around the world.]

Prŷs-Jones, O. & Corbet, S. A. 1991. *Bumblebees.* Naturalists' Handbook 6. Richmond Publishing Co., Slough. 92pp.

[A very comprehensive treatment of the natural history of bumblebees, their distribution in Britain and how to identify them. Very well illustrated, particular feature of this book are the suggestions for original research projects that the layman can usefully carry out.]

Steel, 2001. *Wildflowers for Wildlife Gardening. Osmia* Publications, Banbury. 46pp.

[How to choose and grow wild flowers to encourage wildlife, including bees, into the garden.]

Useful websites – Britain and Europe

www.bwars.com/

The site of the Bees, Wasps and Ants Recording Society (BWARS). Contains much information on the wasps ants and bees native to Britain and Ireland and details of the various national mapping schemes for the distribution of these insects. Members have regular meetings both indoors and in the field and there is a twice-yearly newsletter. The best way to get actively involved in conserving wild bees is to join BWARS.

www.nhm.ac.uk/entomology/bombus

Includes a fully comprehensive and annotated list of all the world's 400 or so bumblebees, compiled by one of the world's leading experts on bumblebees, Dr Paul Williams of the Natural History Museum, London.

www.hymenoptera.com

A German-based site with option in English. Contains very useful information on the natural history of bumblebees, and how to attract them to the garden, including ways of keeping them in artificial nests.

Plate 1

Bombus terrestris, *Buff-tailed bumblebee worker with well filled pollen baskets on knapweed.*

© Ken Preston-Mafham, Premaphotos Wildlife.

Plate 2

Bombus pascuorum, *Common carder bumblebee worker visiting a flower of foxglove* Digitalis purpurea, *whose pollen heavily coats the top of the bees thorax*

Plate 3
Bombus hortorum, *Small garden bumblebee with loaded pollen baskets on a garden nasturtium*, Trapaeolum sp.
© Dr Rod Preston-Mafham, Premaphotos Wildlife.

Plate 4
Bombus lapidaries, Red-tailed bumblebee males on spear thistle, Cirsium vulgare
© Ken Preston-Mafham, Premaphotos Wildlife.

Plate 5

Bombus pratorum,Early bumblebee male [left] and queen on a spear thistle flower

© Ken Preston-Mafham, Premaphotos Wildlife.

Plate 6

Misumena vatia, Flower spider (Thomisidae) female feeding on a bumblebee on common cow wheat.

© Ken Preston-Mafham, Premaphotos Wildlife.

Plate 7

Bombus lucorum, *White-tailed bumblebee queen carrying phoretic deutonymphs of mite* Parasitellus fucorum

© Ken Preston-Mafham, Premaphotos Wildlife.

Plate 8

Volucella bombylans, *Bumblebee plume-horn, a hoverfly (*Syrphidae*), a white-tailed bumblebee mimic.*

© Ken Preston-Mafham, Premaphotos Wildlife.

Plate 9

Psithyrus bohemicus, *Female cuckoo bumblebee breaking open brood cell of host*, Bombus lucorum, *in order to lay eggs.*

Plate 10

Bombus lucorum, *White-tailed bumblebee drinking from the surface of a pond on a hot day.*

Plate 11

Bombus pascuorum, *Common carder bumblebee worker pushing open the hinge of a garden Snapdragon* (Antirrhinum) *flower in the garden.*
© Ken Preston-Mafham, Premaphotos Wildlife.

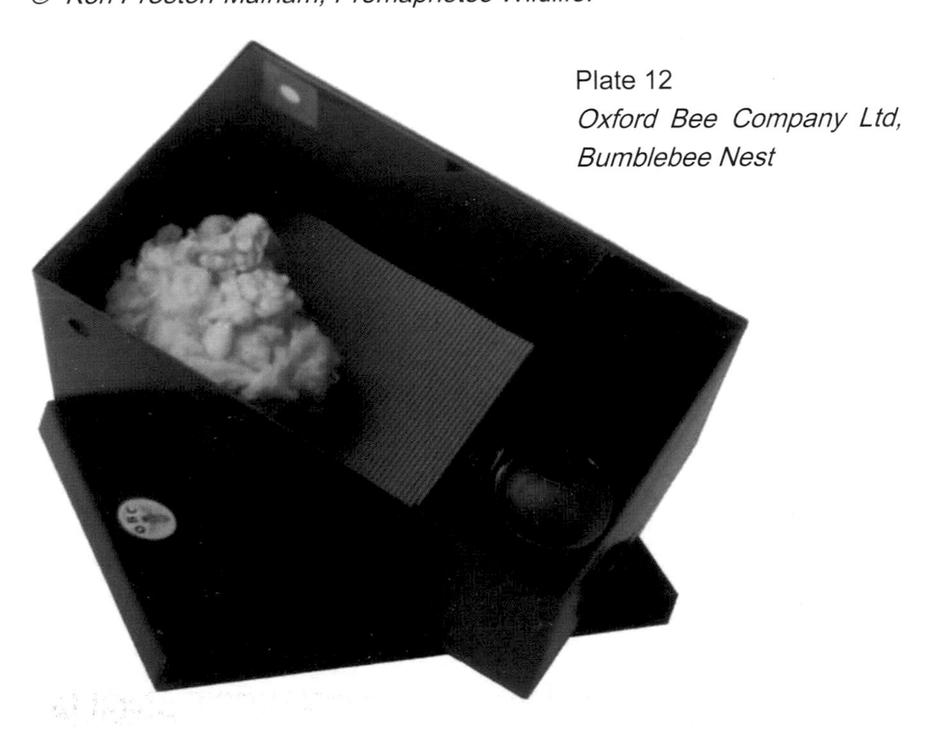

Plate 12

Oxford Bee Company Ltd, Bumblebee Nest